Sandy Creek
NEW YORK

387 Park Avenue South
New York, NY 10016-8810

© 2001 Top That! Publishing plc
This 2011 edition published by Sandy Creek,
by arrangement with Top That! Publishing plc
ISBN 978-1-4351-3800-1
This book is part of the Spy Master kit and is not to be sold separately.
Printed and bound in Shenzhen, Guangdong, China
Manufactured July 2012
Lot 3 5 7 9 10 8 6 4 2

Welcome Agent

This book is your passport to the shadowy world of secret agents and spying.

This book contains information that may or may not be common knowledge. Keep it under wraps. It may prove to be your ticket to inaccessible areas, but the information contained in this book could be used against you if allowed to fall into enemy hands.

As a new recruit, you must ensure that you read the following sections carefully before completing your secret mission on page 33.

Use this section to record details of your own alias.

Code name: . . . .

Date of birth: . . . .

Profession: . . . .

Skills: . . . .

ISSUE DATE
21 MAY 2011
GOVERNMENT AGENCY

WHAT IS A SPY?

A spy is someone who passes secret information on to an agency, government or company that will find it useful. Double agents turn against the organization or agency that recruited them. They will pass information to the enemy agency, while their original employer believes that they are still on their side. They are probably the most devious of all spies.

What makes someone spy?

People may become spies for a number of reasons. Intelligence agencies offer large sums of money to people willing to sell secrets. Other spies may betray their country because they dislike the government or the political system of that country. Some people may be threatened in order to make them spy.

What's it like being a spy?

The real world of spying is not always the glamorous, action-packed lifestyle that is seen in the movies. It is lonely and often boring, but it is still dangerous because if you are discovered, the punishment is very harsh. Spies probably find it difficult to relax!

SPY HISTORY

Spying has taken place for many thousands of years. The leaders of ancient Egypt and the Roman Empire either employed spies, or were sometimes betrayed by spies employed by others.

Agent Caesar

The Roman Emperor Julius Caesar was so keen on secrecy that he invented the Caesar Cipher to send messages to his military leaders abroad.

Shakespearean Spies

Spies were very active in Elizabethan England. Queen Elizabeth I employed Sir Francis Walsingham as a spy master. He was very successful in obtaining secrets from the king of Spain— England's main enemy of the time.

The Ninja
The mysterious Ninja warriors of 15th and 16th century Japan were masters of stealth and disguise (the name ninja means "to become invisible"). Such was their skill, they were believed to possess magical powers that allowed them to disappear into thin air.

Mata Hari
Dutch dancer Margaretha Gertruida Zelle, better known as Mata Hari, was one of the most famous double agents. During the First World War, she learnt the secrets of both the Germans and the French.

Berlin—Spy Capital
The Cold War, when the United States and the Soviet Union were hostile to one another without actually being at war, was a busy time for spies. The German city of Berlin was divided between East and West and was the scene of much spy activity.

U.S. IMMIGRATION
NEW YORK N.Y. 28

NYC HQ 08.01 HOURS

SPY TECHNOLOGY

The nature of a spy's work means that all sorts of gadgets are needed. Devices that are small enough to be hidden away or disguised as something else are an essential part of a spy's toolkit.

Miniature Cameras

Spies use cameras to take pictures of military installations and equipment, secret designs and documents. They are concealed in all sorts of objects, from cigarette packets to umbrellas.

Microdots

Microdots are tiny photographs, usually of secret messages, that are so small they can only be read with a special magnifying viewer. A tiny camera that can easily be hidden is used to take them, and the microdots themselves can be concealed inside objects.

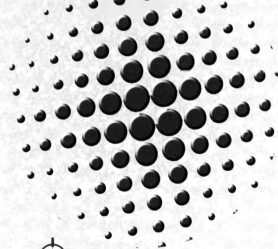

Surveillance

Listening devices, or bugs, are used to pick up secret information. An agent gains access to the room to be bugged and leaves a tiny microphone and transmitter which is able to pick up conversations. A phone tap is a way of listening in on telephone conversations. Tiny video cameras can be used to provide visual evidence as well.

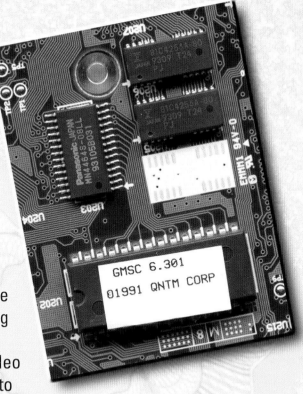

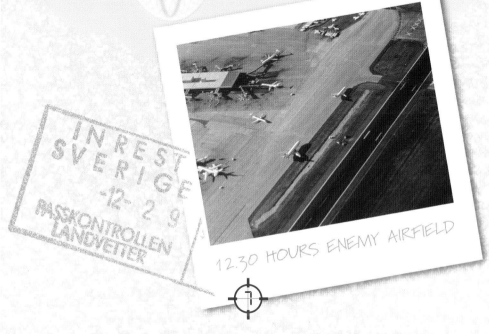

12.30 HOURS ENEMY AIRFIELD

INTELLIGENCE AGENCIES

The best-known spy stories involve the intelligence agencies of various countries.

The **CIA** (Central Intelligence Agency) is the United States' main intelligence agency. It has a network of spies around the world, who gather information about the countries they are stationed in.

MOSSAD is the powerful Israeli secret service. It gathers information about possible threats to that country.

The **KGB** was the name for the Russian secret police. The KGB had spies around the world who gathered political and military information.

MI6 is the name given to the very secretive British Secret Intelligence Service. Its agents work in British embassies around the world.

Agent

TOP SECRET

This secret code section contains all of the codes that you need to complete your secret mission on page 33.

You must not let this book out of your sight. The activities of you and your fellow agents will be at risk should the information contained in this book fall into enemy hands.

End of communication.

SECRET CODES

KEYBOARD CODE

This code is popular among those agents that use a computer. It is based on the way that letters and numbers are arranged on a computer keyboard. The numbers represent any one of the letters directly below them.

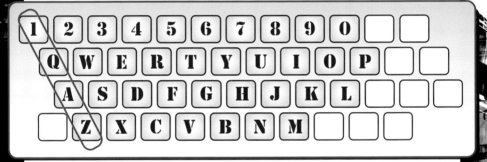

The message:

RELEASE THE VIRUS

Would read:

4393123 563 48472

Most of the numbers represent more than one letter. This means that it will take some logic to work out the message.

SUBSTITUTION CIPHER

This is a fairly simple code, useful for low to medium secure messages. Used by secret agents for some time, it is known as a shift, or substitution cipher. Letters of the alphabet are substituted for others by "shifting" them:

A	B	C	D	E	F	G	H	I	J	K	L	M	N	O	P	Q	R	S	T	U	V	W	X	Y	Z
H	L	M	N	O	P	Q	R	S	T	U	V	W	X	Y	Z	A	B	C	D	E	F	G	H	I	J

To encode a message, the letters from the bottom row are used to represent letters in the message found on the top row.

ANALYZE THE DATA would be encoded as:

A N A L Y Z E   T H E   D A T A

K X K V I J O   D R O   N K D K

PIGPEN CODES

The pigpen code replaces letters of the alphabet with a series of symbols made up of lines and dots. There are several variations of the Pigpen code, and this code has been used by secret societies for centuries. During your mission, you may come across data encoded using the following versions of this code.

Pigpen 1

With this version, **UNDERCOVER AGENT** will read:

U N D E R C O V E R   A G E N T

Pigpen 2

```
 A │ B │ C        J │ K │ L        S │ T │ U
───┼───┼───    ───┼───┼───    ───┼───┼───
·D │ E │ F       :M │ N │ O       ⫶V │ W │ X
───┼───┼───    ───┼───┼───    ───┼───┼───
 G │ H │ I        P │ Q │ R        Y │ Z
```

Using this version of the code, **UNDERCOVER AGENT** will read:

U N D E R C O V E R   A G E N T

Try to decode this top secret message using the code Pigpen 1:

POLYBIUS SQUARE

This code, devised by the Greek historian Polybius, uses a grid to create coordinates that represent each letter of the alphabet as a two-digit number.

To encode a letter, the number of the row that the letter is in creates the first digit. The column number gives the second. Using the Polybius Square, the word **CONSPIRACY** would read:

13.34.33.43.35.24.42.11.13.54

	1	2	3	4	5
1	A	B	C	D	E
2	F	G	H	IJ	K
3	L	M	N	O	P
4	Q	R	S	T	U
5	V	W	X	Y	Z

Note that I and J share the same number.

CYRILLIC TEXT

Using an alternative alphabet is a useful way of disguising a message. This code works by replacing the letters of a regular alphabet with the Cyrillic symbols used in many east European languages. You may come across this code in your dealings with agents from that part of the world.

A	B	C	D	E	F	G	H	I	J	K	L	M
Ф	И	С	В	У	А	П	Р	Ш	О	Л	Д	Ь

N	O	P	Q	R	S	T	U	V	W	X	Y	Z
Т	Щ	З	Й	К	Ы	Е	Г	М	Ц	Ч	Н	Я

Use the Cyrillic symbol code to work out what this cyrillic message says:

ЕРГКЫВФН ФЕ ТЩЩТ

GRID CIPHERS

Top secret messages can be disguised by rearranging the letters using a grid. The message is written in the rows and the message is coded by writing out the columns of the letters.

For instance, to encode the message **HAND OVER THE DATA**, the text is written into a grid:

H A N D O
V E R T H
E D A T A

And the coded message is:

HVE AED NRA DTT OHA

The way that the letters in the code are grouped tells you the size of the grid. Look at this coded message:

M E E T M
E A T T H
E R A I L
W A Y S T
A T I O N

MEEWA EARAT ETAYI TTISO MHLTN

The five groups of five letters fit into a 5 x 5 grid:
(MEET ME AT THE RAILWAY STATION)

TOP SECRET

SECRET CODES

Sometimes, letters that are not part of the message are added to disguise it further:

TTOIT AATRQ HXHPZ EIEOY ATARX

Becomes:

```
T A K E A
T A X I T
O T H E A
I R P O R
T Q Z Y X
```

(TAKE A TAXI TO THE AIRPORT)

The extra letters are Q, Z, Y and X.

Work out what the message says using the Grid Cipher code. Remember to look out for the letters that have been added to confuse enemy spies who may intercept this message.

MNTSQ ETATY EHTEM TEUPZ OSESP

Meet on the statue steps.

OPEN LETTER

Some messages can be concealed within an ordinary-looking letter or e-mail.

Dear Lucy

I'm sorry I can't make it to the movies this weekend, but I've got a nasty virus. The doctor has given me some "special medicine," whatever that is. I promise that we'll go to see the new Bond movie, as soon as it is released. Sorry again!

Carol

TOP SECRET

The last word of each sentence makes the message:

VIRUS IS RELEASED.

A message may also be hidden using the first word of a sentence!

ZIGZAG CIPHER

This code mixes up a message by breaking it up and writing the letters above and below one or more lines. Here's how to disguise the message **DESTROY ALL THE FILES.**

Write the letters like so:

```
  D S R Y L T E I E
. E T O A L H F L S
```

Then write the top line of letters, followed by the bottom line. A period indicates where the top line ends:

DSRYLTEIE.ETOALHFLS

A more complex zigzag cipher uses three lines. The coded message:

TIOETUETE.HFLSNHLPOMSBDSRYD.EETAPTEO

is decoded as:

```
T I O E T U E T E
H F L S N H L P O M S B D S R Y D
  E E T A P T E O
```

[THE FILES ON THE LAPTOP MUST BE DESTROYED]

RB RANDOM BREAK

The random break cipher splits up the letters of a message with unexpected or random spaces. It is not suitable for high-security information, but could easily fool someone who does not know what to look for:

ME ETI NTH ESEC RETA GENTCH ATRO OM

[MEET IN THE SECRET AGENT CHAT ROOM]

NV N VWLS

Another way of disguising a message quickly and easily is to leave out the vowels (A, E, I, O, U). This is often used for text messages sent by a cell phone and is a useful way of disguising a code word.

DWNLD THS SFTWR

[DOWNLOAD THIS SOFTWARE]

TOP SECRET

KEY NUMBER

The key number code is a variation on the grid ciphers. It uses a number to mix up the order of the columns of letters. To decode this message, first number the blocks of coded letters:

EIH UUE ROR TTT TSE HHT
1 2 3 4 5 6

Next, draw up a grid of three rows (because each block has three letters) and six columns (there are six blocks of letters). You also need the key number 461532.

T	H	E	T	R	U
T	H	I	S	O	U
T	T	H	E	R	E
4	6	1	5	3	2

Place the letters in the columns in the numerical order of the key number:

TOP SECRET

This gives you the message **THE TRUTH IS OUT THERE.**

SECRET CODES

21

CODE WORD ALPHABET

Clever use of a grid and a secret code word can create a random alphabet.

An agreed code word is entered into top of the grid. The remaining letters of the alphabet which have not been used are then added.

Code word: **MOTHER**

The alphabet is created by writing out the columns of letters, starting with the one on the left.

M	O	T	H	E	R
A	B	C	D	F	G
I	J	K	L	N	P
Q	S	U	V	W	X
Y	Z				

A	B	C	D	E	F	G	H	I	J	K	L	M	N	O	P	Q	R	S	T	U	V	W	X	Y	Z
M	A	I	Q	Y	O	B	J	S	Z	T	C	K	U	H	D	L	V	E	F	N	W	R	G	P	X

The word INTERNET would read: **SUFYVUYF**

This code combines both a code word and a key number. The letters in the agreed code word are numbered in alphabetical order:

If the code word is **MUNICH**, the letters are rearranged alphabetically to get **CHIMNU**.

M = 4, U = 6, N = 5, I = 3, C = 1, H = 2

Key number: **465312**

The number is written at the top of the grid and the alphabet is entered as shown:

4	6	5	3	1	2
A	B	C	D	E	F
G	H	I	J	K	L
M	N	O	P	Q	R
S	T	U	V	W	X
Y	Z				

An alphabet is created by arranging the letters in the numerical order of the columns.

A	B	C	D	E	F	G	H	I	J	K	L	M	N	O	P	Q	R	S	T	U	V	W	X	Y	Z
E	K	Q	W	F	L	R	X	D	J	P	V	A	G	M	S	Y	C	I	O	U	B	H	N	T	Z

The phrase **TOP SECRET** would be written as:

OMS IFQCFO

MORSE CODE

Morse code represents each letter of the alphabet as a series of dots or dashes.

A	B	C	D	E	F	G
.-	-...	-.-.	-..	.	..-.	--.

H	I	J	K	L	M	N
....	..	.---	-.-	.-..	--	-.

O	P	Q	R	S	T	U
---	.--.	--.-	.-.	...	-	..-

V	W	X	Y	Z
...-	.--	-..-	-.--	--..

WE HAVE CAPTURED AGENT X would be written as:

.-- . .... .- ...- .

-.-. .- .--. - ..- .-. . -..

.- --. . -. - -..-

DOSSIER SECTION

The following dossier pages relate to your mission on page 33.

Top That Spy Academy
Po Box 007

INTERNAL MEMO

To: Senior Agency Personnel

Cc: Personnel dept

Subject: New recruit

We have recruited a new agent into the codebreaking and data analysis department. They are making good progress, but will need to be monitored closely. The recruit has been set a number of tasks and will be assessed upon the completion of those tasks.

Please forward any comments and observations to myself.

S Pye

Agency director

Place your picture here.

Name: Andriy Karpov

Code name: The Block

Date of birth: September 16, 1959

Place of birth: Kiev, Ukraine

....

Description: Karpov is a former soldier who was part of the ultra-secret Soviet Special Operations Unit. Since the break-up of the Soviet Union, he has sold his services to various organizations. His physical appearance and military training mean that he is often employed as an enforcer, although his intelligence gathering abilities should not be underestimated. A keen chess player, Karpov is a shrewd thinker who has outwitted many agents. Karpov has little care for politics or ideas—money determines who he works for.

....

Strengths: his strength!

Weaknesses: money, cheese and onion chips

Key fact: his favorite cartoon character is Scooby Doo

Name: Hugo Cavendish

Code name: Smith

Date of birth: February 21, 1957

Place of birth: Bath, England

....

Description: Oxford educated Cavendish would appear to be the perfect English gentlemen—honorable, honest and decent. This has proved to be an effective cover for one of the world's most cunning secret agents. After Cavendish failed in his application to join MI6, he turned to freelance spying as a way of funding his lavish lifestyle. He is willing to work for most organizations, but is always keen to help those who oppose the country that rejected him. He is highly intelligent, and his knowledge of the world of espionage would be very useful to anyone.

....

Strengths: master of disguise

Weaknesses: luxury yachts, caviar

Key fact: his mother is Russian

Name: Lucy Yeung

Code name: The Doctor

Date of birth: February 21, 1974

Place of birth: Hong Kong, China

....

Description: Dr. Yeung was a promising medical student when she was approached by an organization involved in unethical genetic research. Lured by promises of wealth and power, "The Doctor" moved to the organization's secret laboratory, buried deep inside a Swiss mountain. It is rumored that she remains there, working on cloning a race of super-beings to create the ultimate spy army. Yeung is a ruthless operator who, if her progress goes unchecked, could become one of the world's most powerful and dangerous criminals.

....

Strengths: backed by an army of loyal followers

Weaknesses: hunger for power

Key fact: has an extensive art collection

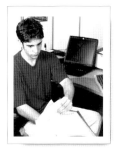

Name: Marlon Oakes

Code name: Zero

Date of birth: April 17, 1983

Place of birth: Detroit, USA

Description: Oakes's parents died when he was very young and he was brought up by his uncle, an electronics pioneer. Able to program a computer before he could write, Oakes is a true technical genius. Since leaving the care of his uncle, Zero (as he likes to be known) has offered his skills to the world's leading cyber-terrorists. Highly-destructive viruses are Zero's speciality and he is rumored to be able to break into even the most secure computer system. While Zero is almost unstoppable behind a computer keyboard, he is weak and vulnerable in a real-life situation.

Strengths: his brain

Weaknesses: new technology, pizza

Key fact: has a microchip in his brain

These newspapers were collected by a fellow agent. The agent went missing before he was able to tell us what relevance they have to your mission. Can you help?

THE GLOBE

SATURDAY MAY 14, 2011

BEWARE OF THE VIRUS!

The Herald

FRIDAY NOVEMBER 4, 2011

AGENT TRAINING IS OVER

The Herald

SUNDAY AUGUST 14, 2011

THIS IS THE REAL THING

The Herald

FRIDAY MAY 27, 2011

ALIEN SPACECRAFT
Handle With Care

THE ECHO

THURSDAY APRIL 7, 2011

BEGIN OPERATION EAGLE WATCH

THE TRIBUNE

TUESDAY FEBRUARY 1, 2011

AWAIT FURTHER INSTRUCTIONS

The Herald
TUESDAY MARCH 29, 2011

STAY UNDERGROUND

The Herald
SUNDAY JUNE 19, 2011

OUR SYSTEM HAS BEEN HACKED

THE ECHO
TUESDAY MAY 17, 2011

ZERO develops new virus

THE TRIBUNE
FRIDAY NOVEMBER 4, 2011

MAP SHOWS LOCATION OF
SECRET BASE

THE GLOBE
TUESDAY FEBRUARY 22, 2011

KARPOV HAS BEEN SIGHTED IN RED SQUARE

Secret Dossier 7

Satellite photographs have been taken in order to investigate reports of UFO sightings in the media.

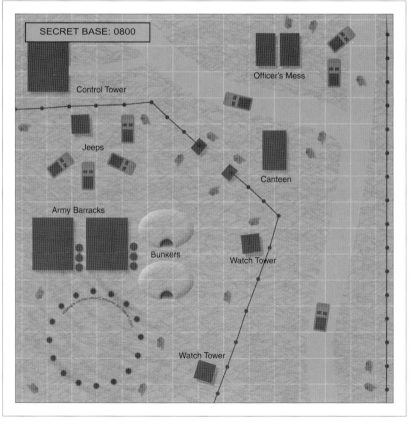

SECRET BASE: 0800

Officer's Mess

Control Tower

Jeeps

Canteen

Army Barracks

Bunkers

Watch Tower

Watch Tower

Agent

This is your Secret Missions file. All of the puzzles in this file can be solved using the Secret Codes and Dossier Sections in this book. Check for the code words which appear at the bottom of each puzzle and then look them up in the Secret Codes Section to find out how to work out the task.

You will also need the following equipment to complete your mission:

Pen or pencil
Notepaper
Magnifying glass (supplied)
Calculator
Binoculars (supplied)
Rearview glasses (supplied)
Disguise mustache (supplied)
Pen torch (supplied)
Secret markers (supplied)
Infrared Decoding card (supplied)
Compass (supplied)

Infrared Decoder Card

Use the infrared decoder card to read the encrypted agent files. Simply place the decoder over an area like the one on the computer screen to reveal the information which is hidden underneath.

Look out for information on the use of other equipment supplied with your kit.

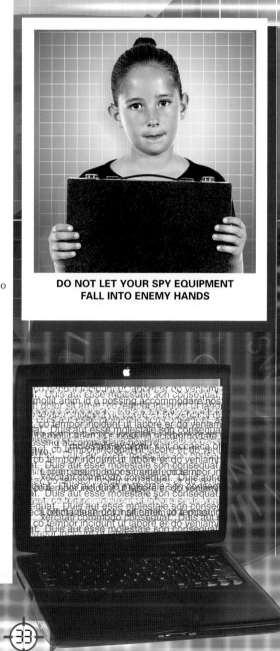

DO NOT LET YOUR SPY EQUIPMENT FALL INTO ENEMY HANDS

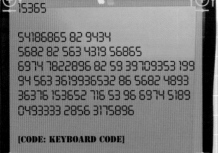

15365

54186865 82 9434
5682 82 563 4319 56865
6974 7822896 82 59 39709353 199
94 563 3619936532 86 5682 4893
36376 153652 716 53 96 6974 5189
0493333 2856 3175896

[CODE: KEYBOARD CODE]

You have received an e-mail on your laptop computer. For obvious security reasons, it has been encrypted. Can you decipher it?

TOP SECRET

ENCRYPTED AGENT FILE 1

Who is this?

MIND GAME

You have obtained a copy of a photograph taken inside an enemy agent's hideaway. The picture shows you several things which will reveal useful information about the agent's identity, activities and whereabouts. Look carefully at the picture (on page 36) for about 30 seconds. Then return to this page and see how much you can remember about the picture by answering the questions below. You will need the magnifying glass for this task.

1. Which landmark can be seen from the window?
2. What is the message on the laptop computer?
3. Which nationality is the agent (according to the passport)?
4. Which newspaper has the agent been reading?
5. What has the agent been eating?
6. Where do you think the agent is heading for?
7. Which language is the agent learning?
8. What important files has the agent obtained?

◀NVISIBLE MESSAGES

The two secret marker pens supplied with your spy kit allow sensitive information to be written invisibly. Only an agent with the developer marker can reveal the message. It is ideal for writing secret codes.

How to use:

1   Write your message using the secret marker.

2   Leave it to dry for 30 seconds.

3   Scribble over the area with the developer marker—the message will reappear.

4   Try writing secret messages between the lines of ordinary letters—blank pieces of paper may look suspicious.

Use this space to test your markers:

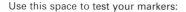

Dear John

Book the seats for us as soon as possible. A flight leaves Heathrow for Madrid on Sunday afternoon. The passports and travelers' checks are all together in my briefcase. Station yourself near the information desk and I'll be there at midday.

Steve.

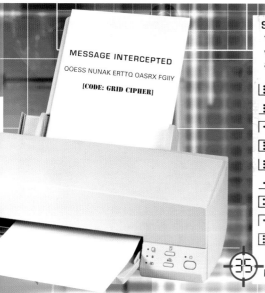

MESSAGE INTERCEPTED

OOESS NUNAK ERTTO OASRX FGIIY

[CODE: GRID CIPHER]

SECRET SYMBOLS

You have intercepted the message below, which you believe reveals more information about something in your secret dossiers.

(message in pigpen cipher symbols)

[CODE: PIGPEN 2]

MIND GAME. SPYCAM: 22.05 NIGHT VISION

ENCRYPTED AGENT FILE 2
Who is this?

THE MATRIX

Cracking this message will tell you more about one of the Secret Dossiers on pages 25-32.

First of all you need to decode these words:

COMBOD	DBSVLI
OKDSXQ	MEZZON
MYVEWX	YBKXQO
BYMUOD	NBYGXC
OPPOMD	OMRYOC

[CODE: SUBSTITUTION CIPHER]

Then using the coordinates from the grid, fit the letters into the spaces below to get the message:

F1	C10	B1			

E3	B2	C7

A1	C10	B4	D9	F9

A6	C10	E1

D6	B4	A7	B2	C2	D2	B4	E9

A8	C5

F1	C10	E4

F9	E7	C4	B6	F8	F5

E6	C8	A1	E1

Fit the words into this grid (the first letter of each word has already been added):

	A	B	C	D	E	F
1	S					
2	E					
3	C					
4	R					
5	E					
6	T					
7	C					
8	O					
9	D					
10	E					

TOP SECRET

Agency HQ has sent the message below. What does it say?

.--- . / .-.. -..- / .-- --- .-. --- .-. .- --..-- / .--- --- .-- .-. .-.

/ .--.- .-. ... .-.. --- .-.- .-. --..-- / .-.. ... . ..-. .-- .--. .-. .--. ----

[CODE: MORSE CODE]

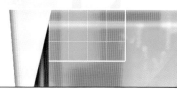

COORDINATES CODE

A message is hidden in the grid below. You'll need your infrared decoder card to reveal the coordinates for the letters.

	A	B	C	D	E	F	G	H	I	J
1	C	X	M	N	T	E	O	R	V	H
2	E	X	E	S	T	M	N	P	A	B
3	M	S	R	Y	Q	V	T	X	A	C
4	N	O	O	N	M	O	L	M	D	T
5	T	B	K	O	Z	N	O	N	L	S
6	O	D	V	P	J	K	L	I	M	N
7	H	C	D	R	W	T	R	N	Q	O
8	G	F	H	S	O	P	M	X	C	X
9	U	G	R	R	S	Q	R	Y	P	T
10	I	J	P	S	U	V	S	T	S	R

ENCRYPTED COORDINATES

MESSAGE INTERCEPTED 2

Your digital radio scanner has picked up a scrambled message. You will need to rearrange the letters once you have decoded them to find the words. It will reveal the worldwide locations of the enemy agents.

DOLS NOEO NWBB LSNO OMIT OCRN

[CODE: GRID CIPHER]

DIGITAL DECEPTION

This numerical message was received on your cell phone. Can you decipher what it says?

12.15.52.11.42.15
34.21
44.23.15
51.24.42.45.43

[CODE: POLYBIUS SQUARE]

There are several useful gadgets supplied with your spy kit. Please take note of the following information before using them in the field.

Binoculars

These agency-issue binoculars are specially designed for use in hostile territory. They can be easily hidden in a pocket.

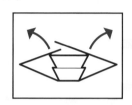

o Carefully unfold the binoculars as shown.

It is important not to attract attention to yourself when using them.

o Hide yourself in bushes, behind trees or walls.

o Beware when using them in sunlight. Light reflecting off the lenses may give your position away.

Never look at the sun!

Rear-vision spectacles

These specially developed rear-vision glasses allow agents to observe suspicious activity taking place behind them. To anyone else, they look like ordinary sunglasses.

o Wear as normal sunglasses.

o The glasses work best in sunlight or brightly lit areas.

o While using the glasses, pretend to read a book or do something similar, so as not to raise suspicion.

Notes: It is rumored that these glasses are based on technology retrieved from a crashed UFO. Can you find information relating to the UFO landing sight in the dossier section on pages 25-32?

Penlight

Many secret missions need to be carried out under cover of darkness. Your penlight can be carried easily in a pocket and it lights an area without giving away your position.

o   Ideal for searching through secret files in dark offices.

o   Small enough to illuminate secret hideaways.

o   Use it to alert a fellow agent to your position.

Compass

The compass supplied can help you to find your way in unknown territory.

o   The compass always lines up with north/south.

o   It is particularly useful when used with a map.

Disguise mustache

It is important not to attract attention while on a secret mission. The disguise mustache supplied with your kit will help you to hide your identity.

o   Wearing a hat, dark glasses and an overcoat will make your disguise even more effective.

o   Act naturally. You need to blend in with your surroundings and not arouse the suspicion of others.

MAN SEEN LEAVING SECRET AGENT'S HOUSE—NOTHING SUSPICIOUS

TOP SECRET

39

You have received the following message from your contact in Moscow. You believe it is information about the whereabouts of one of the enemy agents.

ЛФКЗЩМ РФЫ ИУУТ ЫШПРЕУВ ШТ КУВ ЫЙГФКУ

[CODE: CYRILLIC TEXT]

AUTHORIZED
PERSONNEL
ONLY

ENCRYPTED AGENT FILE 3

Who is this?

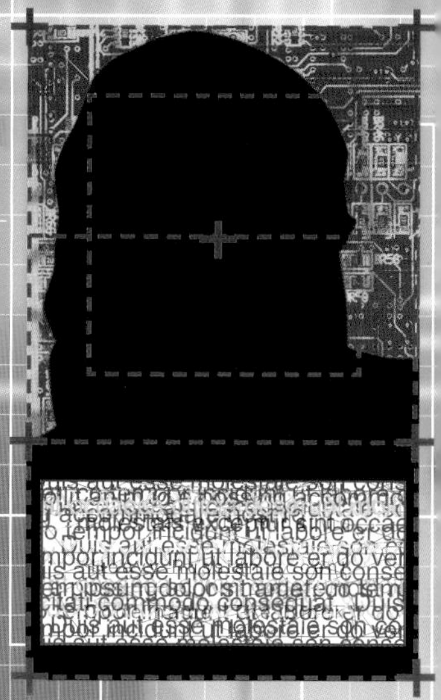

SICKNOTE

Our sources suggest that there is more to this note from a grandmother to her grandson.

Dear Jimmy

Just a little note to see how you are, that's all. My eyesight is getting quite bad now and I just can't get used to these new contacts. I'm a having a little rest while I wait for the nurse to return. Anyway, I'm feeling much better now and cannot wait to get home.

Lots of love

Gran

[CODE: OPEN LETTER]

SECRET SYMBOL 2

While in a forest investigating a mysterious incident, you find a strange piece of metal with the following symbols on it. What do they mean?

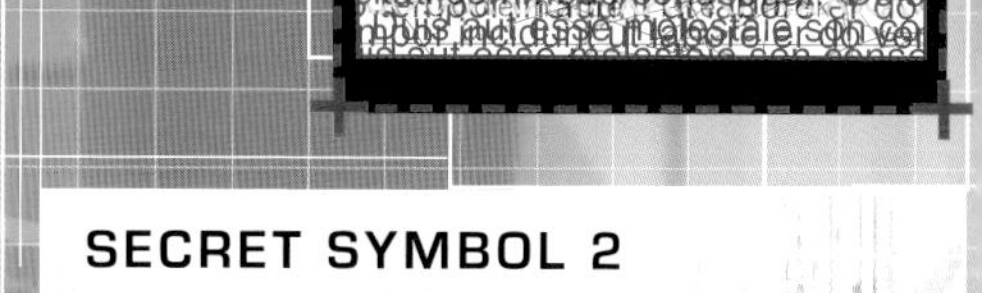

[CODE: PIGPEN]

Agency HQ has contacted you with an urgent message. Can you decipher it?

SURUWFHNUO.TYNEGONAATUTEISRCIN.ADRDIRRTTS

[CODE: ZIGZAG CIPHER]

CLOSE UP

Use your magnifying glass to study this scene carefully. How many suspicious characters can you see at work?

The dossier section may hold the key to this surveillance picture.

CALCULATOR CODES

You will need to use a calculator to solve these codes. The calculations will give you a key number to interpret the messages.

1 EETT DACC NMOA SNLN AIOT
   $(20382 - 37 \times 2 + 635 = ?)$

2. LONH CCUS OTMA ECTQ LDET
   $(6085 - 452 \times 4 + 982 = ?)$

3 THSS ARMG AFES ITEE WURA
   $(18715 - 821 \times 2 - 547 = ?)$

[CODE: KEY NUMBER]

To crack each one of these coded messages, you will need to solve the clues to reveal a code word. Clue: each one is a city.

1 This city was once called New Amsterdam.
EGBXG JAG WZPQLGSJC AGTG

2 This city was once known as the spy capital of the world.
GYHTW DJYVALTDW YAHKY CALMN

3 The river Seine runs through this city.
QBPIVH BGUHR UZVHBRSUP

[CODE: CODE WORD AND KEY NUMBER]

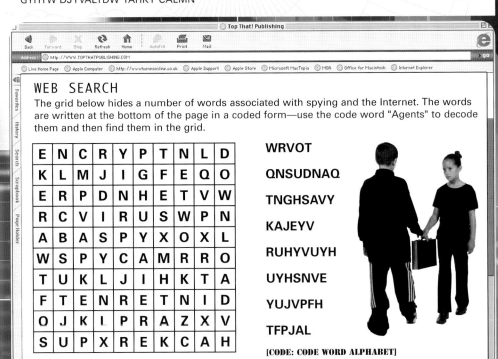

WEB SEARCH

The grid below hides a number of words associated with spying and the Internet. The words are written at the bottom of the page in a coded form—use the code word "Agents" to decode them and then find them in the grid.

E	N	C	R	Y	P	T	N	L	D
K	L	M	J	I	G	F	E	Q	O
E	R	P	D	N	H	E	T	V	W
R	C	V	I	R	U	S	W	P	N
A	B	A	S	P	Y	X	O	X	L
W	S	P	Y	C	A	M	R	R	O
T	U	K	L	J	I	H	K	T	A
F	T	E	N	R	E	T	N	I	D
O	J	K	I	P	R	A	Z	X	V
S	U	P	X	R	E	K	C	A	H

WRVOT

QNSUDNAQ

TNGHSAVY

KAJEYV

RUHYVUYH

UYHSNVE

YUJVPFH

TFPJAL

[CODE: CODE WORD ALPHABET]

UPDATE FROM HQ

You receive two messages from HQ on your cell phone. Can you read them?

WEH AVEC APTU REDS MIT HHEH ASGIV EN USSO MEUS EFULINF ORM ATI ON

R SYSTM HS BN HCKD

[CODE: RANDOM BREAK & N VWLS]

MICRO MESSAGE

Use your magnifying glass to read this message from Moscow.

[CODE: CYRILLIC TEXT]

DIGITAL 2 DECEPTION

This message has come from the Agency's technical department. Can you decipher it?

23 6143 8336584833 563 48472 163 332549633 85

[CODE: KEYBOARD CODE]

ENCRYPTED AGENT FILE 4

Who is this?

CROSSWORD CODE

Once you have deciphered these number codes, you should be able to fit the words into the grid. Some of the letters have been added for you.

13.11.32.15.42.11
51.24.42.45.43
15.51.24.14.15.33.13.15
13.42.11.13.25.15.14
13.34.14.15.43
14.34.13.45.32.15.33.44
43.35.24.15.43

[CODE: POLYBIUS SQUARE]

C

S

E

You have managed to intercept another message between enemy agents. It contains some worrying news.

ZAEDV ESLAI RDONR OEPEU HVEWS

[CODE: GRID CIPHER]

DOUBLE VISION

A copy has been made of a top-secret blueprint of a new kind of aircraft. We believe that it has been tampered with. You may need to use your magnifying glass to identify some of the irregularities. (There are five to spot.)

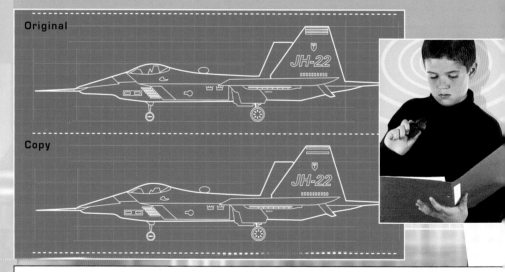

Original

JH-22

Copy

JH-22

EXCHANGE RATE

The number below will help you to decode the names of four currencies that you may use on your missions. When you have worked them out, write them next to the flag of the country that uses that currency.

614253

OOUR LNLY RREN LUBO ADEE DPOU

[CODE: KEY NUMBER]

You have been taken hostage by enemy agents. Try to escape before you are interrogated. If you follow more than two dead end routes you will be recaptured.

CURRENT LOCATION

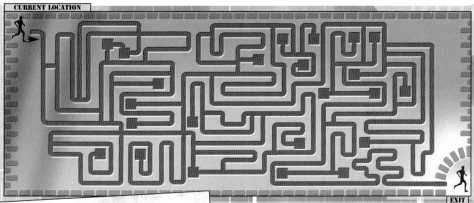

EXIT

SUB SNAKE

When you have worked out what the coded words below are, fit them into the snake-like grid.

UQL
LOBVSX
XEMVOKB
NSCU
KQOXD
DBKZ
BECCSK

[CODE: SUBSTITUTION CIPHER]

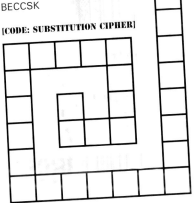

PAY DAY

The agency is trying to contact you about your fee. What does it say?

TEGNYILAOEILOD
LASITYUACUT.HA
ECWLPYNMLINOL
RNOORCON

[CODE: ZIGZAG CIPHER]

Can you spot the five differences between these two surveillance pictures?

SECRET SYMBOL 3

You have intercepted another message from the enemy agents. What does the message say?

[CODE: PIGPEN 2]

EMAIL CODE

The final message of your mission is from Agency HQ. It has come via email on your laptop.

52.15.31.31
14.34.33.15
11.22.15.33.44
54.34.45
23.11.51.15
43.45.13.13.15.43.43.21.45.31.31.54
13.34.32.35.31.15.44.15.14
54.34.45.42
32.24.43.43.24.34.33

[CODE: POLYBIUS SQUARE]

OPEN MESSAGE

Can you find the message hidden in this letter?

Dear Harry

It was great to get that news from you out of the blue. I was absolutely over the Moon. I'm feeling a bit hungry now, so I'm off to the cafe. See you on Saturday!

Ben

[CODE: OPEN LETTER]

MESSAGE DETECTED
AGENT
TRAINING IS OVER
THIS IS THE REAL THING
YOUR MISSION IS TO COMPLETE ALL OF THE
CHALLENGES IN THIS FILE
ENEMY AGENTS MAY BE ON YOUR TAIL
PROCEED WITH CAUTION

ENCRYPTED AGENT FILE 1
HUGO CAVENDISH

MIND GAME
1. EIFFEL TOWER
2. VIRUS READY FOR RELEASE
3. UK
4. SPYING TIMES
5. PIZZA
6. CAPE TOWN
7. RUSSIAN
8. MILITARY BLUEPRINT

SECRET SYMBOLS
THE CRASHED SPACE SHIP IS A HOAX
WE SET IT UP TO DIVERT ATTENTION FROM OUR
ACTIVITY IT SEEMS TO HAVE WORKED

MESSAGE INTERCEPTED
ONE OF OUR AGENTS IS AT RISK

ENCRYPTED AGENT FILE 2
MARLON OAKES

THE MATRIX
THE MAP SHOWS THE LOCATION OF THE
SECRET BASE

DOT DASH
WE ARE MONITORING YOUR PROGRESS
CAREFULLY

COORDINATES CODE
SEND THE DISK TO YOUR CONTACT

MESSAGE INTERCEPTED 2
LONDON
MOSCOW
BERLIN
BOSTON

DIGITAL DECEPTION
BEWARE OF THE VIRUS

FOREIGN AFFAIRS
KARPOV HAS BEEN SIGHTED IN RED SQUARE

ENCRYPTED AGENT FILE 3
ANDRIY KARPOV

SICKNOTE
ALL CONTACTS RETURN HOME

SECRET SYMBOL 2
ALIEN SPACECRAFT
HANDLE WITH CARE

WARNING
STAY UNDERGROUND
AWAIT FURTHER INSTRUCTIONS

CLOSE UP
ANDRIY KARPOV
HUGO CAVENDISH
LUCY YEUNG
MARLON OAKES

CALCULATOR CODES
1 41325: SEND AN EMAIL TO CONTACT
2 23514: COLLECT DOCUMENTS AT HQ
3 35241: AWAIT FURTHER MESSAGES

WORLD WORDS
1 New York
  LEAVE THE DOCUMENTS HERE
2 Berlin
  BEGIN OPERATION EAGLE WATCH
3 Paris
  DANGER ABORT OPERATION

WEB SEARCH

E	N	C	R	Y	P	T	N	L	D
K	L	M	J	I	G	F	E	Q	O
E	R	P	D	N	H	E	T	V	W
R	C	V	I	R	U	S	W	P	N
A	B	A	S	P	Y	X	O	X	L
W	S	P	Y	C	A	M	R	R	O
T	U	K	L	J	I	H	K	T	A
F	T	E	N	R	E	T	N	I	D
O	J	K	L	P	R	A	Z	X	V
S	U	P	X	R	E	K	C	A	H

UPDATE FROM HQ
WE HAVE CAPTURED SMITH HE HAS GIVEN US
SOME USEFUL INFORMATION

OUR SYSTEM HAS BEEN HACKED

MICRO MESSAGE
KARPOV HAS GIVEN HIMSELF UP BUT WE DO NOT TRUST HIM

DIGITAL DECEPTION 2
WE HAVE IDENTIFIED THE VIRUS AND DESTROYED IT

ENCRYPTED AGENT FILE 4
LUCY YEUNG

CROSSWORD CODE

MESSAGE INTERCEPTED 3
ZERO HAS DEVELOPED A NEW VIRUS

DOUBLE VISION

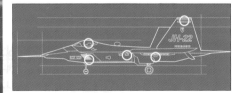

EXCHANGE RATE
DOLLAR
POUND
ROUBLE
EURO
YEN

UNDERGROUND LABYRINTH

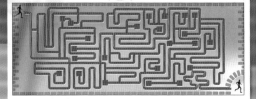

SUB SNAKE
WORDS:

PAY DAY
THE AGENCY WILL PAY ONE MILLION DOLLARS INTO YOUR ACCOUNT

SECRET MEET

SECRET SYMBOL 3
WE HAVE FOUND A REAL UFO THIS IS NOT A HOAX

OPEN MESSAGE
BLUE MOON CAFÉ
SATURDAY

EMAIL CODE
WELL DONE AGENT YOU HAVE COMPLETED YOUR MISSION SUCCESSFULLY